ART OF THE T[A]

2008

Introduction

The Visconti Tarot Cards have long been considered the most important example of fifteenth-century playing cards, though up until recent times the Tarot Cards of Charles VI, supposedly of French origin, were believed to be the oldest. In 1906 these beautiful cards, now in the National Library, Paris, were correctly and definitively ascribed to the Estensi court of Ferrara and redated c. 1470.

Thanks to this attribution, the Visconti Tarot Cards return to being the oldest pack surviving from a marvelous era. During this period, the Italian courts would compete among themselves in pomp and munificence, spending exorbitant sums on games to amuse the courtiers. Consequently, every card in this pack is a unique work of art elaborately produced. Undoubtedly conceived by Humanist scholars, these works of art were rendered by the artists typically commissioned to paint portraits, frescoes, or illuminated manuscripts. Eventually, production of these packs became cost-prohibitive, and they were abandoned in favor of less extravagant cards.

Less expensive packs did exist even in the princely courts, but being widely used, they quickly became dirty and creased and were discarded. The cards produced with sophisticated techniques and quality materials have endured centuries of handling almost intact. There are still sixteen packs of tarot cards attributed to Visconti commissions in various public and private collections, although none of them is complete. Of these, the most famous is the Visconti Tarot Cards, although the name is really too generic in that the pack has been identified with much greater precision.

The Visconti Tarot Cards

The oldest pack of tarot cards created for the lords of Milan in the fifteenth century is called the Visconti di Modrone pack, after its original owner. Of the Visconti di Modrone pack, sixty-five out of the seventy-eight that theoretically make up a complete pack have survived: of these, only eleven are trumps. The pack has been dated, almost unanimously, to about 1441, during the dukedom of Filippo Maria Visconti (1392–1447).

The Visconti di Modrone cards are unique in that they show unconventional subjects, like the three theological virtues: Faith, Hope, and Charity. This suggests that the pack may have been a prototype subsequently abandoned, although others believe that it was merely a variant of a pre-existing model. The so-called Brambilla pack, c. 1447, conserved in the Brera Gallery in Milan, is similar to the Visconti di Modrone pack. Forty-eight cards remain, including just two trumps: the Emperor and the Wheel of Fortune. However, neither the Visconti di Modrone nor the Brambilla packs were copied by card painters, perhaps because their images were excessively complex and detailed. The Milanese figurative tradition looked to the Visconti-Sforza pack: seventy-four cards remain divided among New York's Pierpont Morgan Library, the Carrara Academy in Bergamo, and the private collection of the Colleoni family.

Its fame is certainly warranted in that it is the most complete of all the illuminated packs. Only four cards are missing: the Devil, the Tower, the 3 of Swords, and the Knight of Pentacles. Many cards bear Sforza emblems and Visconti symbols, but the three entwined rings decorating the cloak of the Emperor and Empress is the principal element linking this pack to the 1441 union of Francesco Sforza and Bianca Maria Visconti, Filippo Maria's natural daughter. The merging of personal emblems with such symbols of ducal power as the palm and the laurel suggests that the pack was realized after Francesco succeeded to the leadership of the duchy of Milan in 1450. Documents in the Sforzesco Ducal Archives provide further confirmation of this.

The importance of the Visconti-Sforza Tarot Cards is the fact that they served as a model for all subsequent illuminated trumps realized for the Milanese court. By far the most famous in the world, this pack is the subject of our study.

Published by Barnes & Noble, Inc.
2007 Barnes & Noble
122 Fifth Avenue
New York, NY 10011
(212) 633-3300

ISBN: 0-7607-9282-8

Artwork: Visconti Tarot; © Lo Scarabeo, Italy; Milan, 1450 ca;
restored by Atanas A. Atanassov; www.loscarabeo.com

Printed in Singapore

_____

Lunar phases and equinoxes are given in Universal Time.

Lunar Phases

● New Moon

☾ First Quarter Moon

○ Full Moon

☽ Last Quarter Moon

(ACT, AUS) National Capital, Australia   (AUS) Australia   (CAN) Canada   (EU) Europe
(FRA) France   (GBR) Great Britain: England, Scotland, Wales   (IRL) Ireland   (MEX) Mexico
(NSW) New South Wales, Australia   (N HEM) Northern Hemisphere   (N IRL) Northern Ireland
(NT AUS) Northern Territory, Australia   (NZL) New Zealand   (Qland) Queensland, Australia
(SCT) Scotland   (S AUS) Southern Australia   (S HEM) Southern Hemisphere
(TAS AUS) Tasmania, Australia   (USA) United States   (W AUS) Western Australia

Personal Data

Name

Address

Tel
Cell
Fax
Email

Company

Address

Tel
Fax
Email

Notes

World Time Differences

Abu Dhabi	+4	Edmonton	−7	New Delhi	+5½
Accra	0	Frankfurt	+1	New York	−5
Addis Ababa	+3	Freetown	0	Oslo	+1
Alexandria	+2	Geneva	+1	Ottawa	−5
Algiers	+1	Glasgow	0	Paris	+1
Amman	+1	Halifax	−4	Port-au-Prince	−5
Amsterdam	+1	Harare	+2	Prague	+1
Anchorage	−9	Havana	−5	Pyonyang	+9
Antigua	−4	Helsinki	+2	Rangoon	+6
Athens	+2	Hong Kong	+8	Reykjavik	0
Atlanta	−5	Honolulu	−10	Rio de Janeiro	−3
Auckland	+11	Houston	−6	Riyadh	+3
Azores	−1	Islamabad	+5	Rome	+1
Baghdad	+3	Istanbul	+2	Saigon	+7
Baku	+4	Jakarta	+7	San Juan	−4
Bangkok	+7	Jerusalem	+2	Santiago	−3
Barcelona	+1	Johannesburg	+2	São Paulo	−2
Basra	+3	Kabul	+4	Sarajevo	+1
Beijing	+8	Karachi	+5	Saskatchewan	−6
Belfast	0	Katmandu	+4	Seoul	+9
Belize City	−6	Khartoum	+2	Shanghai	+8
Berlin	+1	Kuala Lumpur	+8	Singapore	+8
Bern	+1	Kuwait	+3	Sofia	+2
Bogota	−5	Lagos	0	Stockholm	+1
Bombay	+5½	La Paz	−4	St. Louis	−6
Brussels	+1	Lebanon	+2	St. Petersburg	+3
Budapest	+1	Lima	−5	Sydney	+11
Buenos Aires	−3	Lisbon	0	Taipei	+8
Cairo	+2	Ljubljana	+1	Teheran	+3½
Calcutta	+5½	London	0	Timbuktu	0
Calgary	−7	Los Angeles	−8	Tokyo	+9
Caracas	−4	Madrid	+1	Toronto	−5
Casablanca	0	Managua	−6	Tunis	+1
Chicago	−6	Manila	+8	Ulan Bator	+8
Copenhagen	+1	Martinique	−4	Vancouver	−8
Curaçao	−4	Melbourne	+11	Vienna	+1
Dakar	0	Mexico City	−6	Vladivostok	+10
Damascus	+2	Mogadishu	+3	Volgograd	+4
Dar es Salaam	+3	Montevideo	−3	Warsaw	+1
Denver	−7	Montreal	−5	Winnipeg	−6
Dublin	0	Moscow	+3	Yokohama	+9
Edinburgh	0	Nairobi	+3	Zurich	+1

*Time differences are based on Greenwich Mean Time, Winter Standard Time.

International Dialing Codes

Afghanistan*	93	Estonia	372	Israel 972
Algeria	213	Ethiopia	251	Haifa 4
American Samoa*	684	Addis Ababa	1	Jerusalem 2
Andorra*	376	Fiji*	679	Tel Aviv 3

Afghanistan*	93

Afghanistan* 93 Estonia 372 Israel 972 New Zealand 64 Switzerland 41
Algeria 213 Ethiopia 251 Haifa 4 Auckland 9 Basel 61
American Samoa* 684 Addis Ababa 1 Jerusalem 2 Christchurch 3 Geneva 22
Andorra* 376 Fiji* 679 Tel Aviv 3 Wellington 4 Lausanne 21
Argentina 54 Finland 358 Italy 39 Nicaragua 505 Zurich 1
Buenos Aires 11 Helsinki 9 Florence 055 Managua 2 Tahiti* 689
Australia 61 France 33 Milan 02 Nigeria 234 Taiwan 886
Melbourne 03 Paris 1 Rome 06 Norway* 47 Taipei 2
Sydney 02 Northwest France 2 Venice 041 Oman* 968 Tanzania 255
Austria 43 Northeast France 3 Japan 81 Pakistan 92 Thailand 66
Salzburg 662 Southeast France 4 Hiroshima 82 Islamabad 51 Bangkok 2
Vienna 1 Southwest France 5 Kawasaki 44 Panama* 507 Tunisia 216
Bahrain* 973 French Antilles* 596 Nagoya 52 Papua New Guinea* 675 Tunis 1
Belgium 32 French Polynesia* 689 Tokyo 3 Paraguay 595 Turkey 90
Antwerp 3 Gabon* 241 Yokohama 45 Asunción 21 Ankara 312
Brussels 2 Germany 49 Jordan 962 Peru 51 Istanbul 212, 216
Liège 4 Berlin 30 Amman 6 Lima 1 Uganda 256
Belize 501 Bonn 228 Kenya 254 Philippines 63 United Arab
Bolivia 591 Cologne 221 Nairobi 2 Manila 2 Emirates 971
Santa Cruz 33 Dresden 351 Korea, Republic of 82 Poland 48 Abu Dhabi 2
Brazil 55 Frankfurt 69 Seoul 2 Warsaw 22 Dubai 4
Brasilandia 61 Hanover 511 Kuwait* 965 Portugal 351 United Kingdom 44
Rio de Janeiro 21 Munich 89 Lesotho* 266 Lisbon 1 Belfast 1232
São Paulo 11 Nurnberg 911 Liberia* 231 Porto 2 Birmingham 121
Brunei 673 Gibraltar* 350 Libya 218 Qatar* 974 Edinburgh 131
Cameroon* 237 Greece 30 Tripoli 21 Romania 40 Glasgow 141
Canada** - Athens 01 Liechtenstein* 423 Bucharest 21 Liverpool 151
Montreal 514 Guam* 1+671 Luxembourg* 352 Russia 7 London 207, 208
Ottawa 613 Guantanamo Bay* 5399 Malawi 265 Moscow 095 Manchester 161
Quebec 418 Guatemala* 502 Domasi 531 St. Petersburg 812 United States
Toronto 416, 647 Guyana 592 Malaysia 60 St. Pierre & of America 1
Chile 56 Georgetown 2 Kuala Lumpur 3 Miquelon 508 Uruguay 598
Santiago 2 Haiti* 509 Mexico 52 San Marino 378 Montevideo 2
China, Republic of 86 Honduras* 504 Acapulco 744 Saudi Arabia 966 Vatican City 396
Beijing 10 Hungary 36 Cancun 988 Mecca 2 Venezuela 58
Canton 20 Budapest 1 Mexico City 55 Riyadh 3 Caracas 212
Hong Kong 852 Iceland* 354 Monaco 3393 Senegal* 221 San Cristobal 76
Colombia 57 India 91 Morocco 212 Singapore* 65 Valencia 241
Bogota 1 Calcutta 33 Casablanca 2 Spain 34 Yemen 967
Costa Rica* 506 Mumbai 22 Marrakech 4 Barcelona 93 Amran 7
Côte d'Ivoire* 225 New Delhi 11 Rabat 77 Madrid 91 Yugoslavia 381
Cyprus 357 Indonesia 62 Namibia 264 Seville 95 Belgrade 11
Nicosia 2 Jakarta 21 Netherlands, The 31 Sri Lanka 94 Zambia 260
Czech Republic 420 Iran 98 Amsterdam 20 Kandy 8 Zimbabwe 263
Prague 2 Teheran 21 Otterlo 318 Suriname* 597
Denmark* 45 Iraq 964 Rotterdam 10 Swaziland* 268
Ecuador 593 Baghdad 1 The Hague 70 Sweden 46
Quito 2 Ireland 353 Netherlands Antilles 599 Gothenberg 31
Egypt 20 Dublin 1 Aruba 297 Stockholm 8
Cairo 2 Killarney 64 Curaçao 599
El Salvador* 503 Tipperary 62 New Caledonia* 687

To place an international telephone call, dial the international access code (011 in the U.S.), the country code number, and then the local number.

*City routing code not required.

**International access code not required when dialing from the United States.

North American Area Codes

Alaska	907	Greensboro, AL	334
Albany, NY	518	Hackensack, NJ 201, 551	
Altoona, PA	814	Hagerstown, MD 240, 301	
Amarillo, TX	806	Harrisburg, PA	717
Arkansas 501, 870, 479		Hartford, CT	860
Arlington, VA 571, 703		Hawaii	808
Arlington, TX 682, 817		Hempstead, NY	516
Aspen, CO	970	Houston,	
Atlanta,		TX 281, 713, 832	
GA 404, 470, 678		Huntsville, AL	256
Austin, TX	512	Idaho	208
Bakersfield, CA	661	Indianapolis, IN	317
Baltimore, MD 410, 443		Jackson, MS	601
Bellevue, WA	425	Jacksonville, FL	904
Biloxi, MS	228	Jacksonville, NC	910
Binghamton, NY —	607	Jonesboro, AR	870
Birmingham, AL	205	Kansas City, MO	816
Boston, MA 617, 857		Lansing, MI	517
Bristol, CT	860	Las Vegas, NV	702
Buffalo, NY	716	Lexington, KY	859
Centralia, IL	618	Little Rock, AR	501
Charlotte, NC 704, 980		Long Beach, CA	562
Charleston, SC	843	Longview, TX	903
Chicago,		Louisville, KY	502
IL 312, 630, 708, 773		Los Angeles,	
Cincinnati, OH	513	CA 213, 323	
Clemson, SC	864	Madison, WI	608
Cleveland, OH	216	Maine	207
Colorado Springs,		Memphis, TN	901
CO	719	Miami, FL 305, 786	
Columbia, SC	803	Milwaukee, WI	414
Columbus, OH	614	Minneapolis, MN	612
Council Bluffs, IA	712	Mississippi	228,
Covington, KY	859		601, 662
Dallas,		Montana	406
TX 214, 469, 972		Nashville, TN	615
Delaware	302	Newark, NJ 862, 973	
Denver, CO 303, 720		New Brunswick,	
Des Moines, IA	515	NJ 732, 848	
Detroit, MI	313	New Castle, PA	724
Dubuque, IA	563	New Hampshire	603
Duluth, MN	218	New Haven, CT	203
Eau Claire, WI	715	New Mexico	505
Escanaba, MI	906	New Orleans, LA	504
Evansville, IN	812	New York, NY	
Fort Myers, FL	239	Manhattan 212,	
Fort Worth, TX 682, 817		646, 917	
Fresno, CA	559	Bronx, Brooklyn,	
Galveston, TX	409	Queens, Staten	
Grand Rapids, MI	616	Island 347, 718, 917	

North Dakota	701	Sweetwater, TX	325
North Platte, NE	308	Syracuse, NY	315
Oakland, CA	510	Tacoma, WA	253
Oklahoma City, OK	405	Tampa, FL	813
Omaha, NE	402	Toledo, OH 419, 567	
Orange, CA	714	Topeka, KS	785
Oregon 503, 541, 971		Trenton, NJ	609
Orlando, FL 321, 407		Tulsa, OK	918
Pasadena, CA	626	Tucson, AZ	520
Pensacola, FL	850	Utah 435, 801	
Peoria, IL	309	Vermont	802
Philadelphia,		Waco, TX	254
PA 215, 267		Washington, DC	202
Pittsburgh, PA 412, 878		West Virginia	304
Phoenix,		White Plains, NY	914
AZ 480, 602, 623		Wichita, KS	316
Portland, OR 503, 971		Worcester, MA 508, 774	
Poughkeepsie, NY	845	Wyoming	307
Raleigh, NC	919	Yuma, AZ	928
Reading, PA 484, 610			
Reno, NV	775	**CANADA**	
Rhode Island	401	Alberta 403, 780	
Richmond, VA	804	British Columbia	
Rochester, MN	507	250, 604, 778	
Rochester, NY	585	Calgary, AB	403
Rockford, IL	815	Edmonton, AB	780
Sacramento, CA	916	London, ON	519
Salt Lake City, UT	801	Manitoba	204
San Antonio, TX	210	Montreal, PQ	514
San Diego,		Nunavut Territory	867
CA 619, 760, 858		New Brunswick	506
San Francisco, CA	415	Newfoundland	709
San Jose, CA	408	North Bay, ON	705
Santa Monica, CA	310	Northwest Territory	867
Santa Rosa, CA	707	Nova Scotia	902
Savannah, GA	912	Ottawa, ON	613
Seattle, WA	206	Prince Edward Is.	902
Shreveport, LA	318	Quebec, PQ	418
Silver Spring,		Saskatchewan	306
MD 240, 301		Sherbrooke, PQ	819
Smithtown, NY	631	Thunder Bay, ON	807
South Bend, IN	574	Toronto, ON 416, 647	
South Dakota	605	Vancouver, BC 604, 778	
Spokane, WA	509	Yukon Territory	867
Springfield, IL	217		
Springfield, MA	413	**BAHAMAS**	242
Springfield, MO	417	**BERMUDA**	441
St. Louis, MO	314	**DOMINICAN**	
St. Paul, MN	651	**REPUBLIC**	809
St. Petersburg, FL	727		

Please note: New telephone area codes may have been added since printing. Check with local operator if necessary.

Weights & Measures

Length

1 inch (in)		= 2.54 cm
1 foot (ft)	= 12 in	= 0.3048 m
1 yard (yd)	= 3 ft	= 0.9144 m
1 mile (mi)	= 1760 yd	= 1.6093 km
1 nautical mile	= 6,076.115 ft	= 1.852 km
1 millimeter (mm)		= 0.0394 in
1 centimeter (cm)	= 10 mm	= 0.3937 in
1 decimeter (dm)	= 10 cm	= 3.937 in
1 meter (m)	= 100 cm	= 1.0936 yd
1 kilometer (km)	= 1,000 m	= 0.6214 mi

Area

1 square inch (in^2)		= 6.4516 cm^2
1 square foot (ft^2)	= 144 in^2	= 0.0929 m^2
1 square yard (yd^2)	= 9 ft^2	= 0.8361 m^2
1 acre	= 4840 yd^2	= 4046.87 m^2
1 square mile (mi^2)	= 640 acres	= 2.59 km^2
1 square centimeter (cm^2)	= 100 mm^2	= 0.1550 in^2
1 square meter (m^2)	= 10,000 cm^2	= 1.1959 yd^2
1 hectare (ha)	= 10,000 m^2	= 2.471 acres
1 square kilometer (km^2)	= 100 ha	= 0.3861 mi^2

Volume

1 cubic inch (in^3)		= 16.387 cm^3
1 cubic foot (ft^3)	= 1728 in^3	= 0.0283 m^3
1 cubic yard (yd^3)	= 27 ft^3	= 0.7645 m^3
1 cubic centimeter (cm^3)	= 0.0610 in^3	
1 cubic decimeter (dm^3)	= 1,000 cm^3	= 0.0353 ft^3
1 cubic meter (m^3)	= 1,000 dm^3	= 1.3079 yd^3

Mass

1 ounce (oz)	= 437.5 grains	= 28.349 g
1 pound (lb)	= 16 oz	= 0.4536 kg
1 short ton	= 2,000 lbs	= 0.9072 t
1 long ton	= 2,240 lbs	= 1.0160 t
1 gram (g)	= 1,000 mg	= 0.0352 oz
1 kilogram (kg)	= 1,000 g	= 2.2046 lb
1 metric ton (t)	= 1,000 kg	= 1.1023 short tons

Capacity

1 US dry pint (pt)	= 0.5 dry qt	= 0.5506 l
1 US dry quart (qt)	= 2 US dry pt	= 1.101 l
1 US bushel (bu)	= 64 US dry pt	= 35.239 l
1 US fluid ounce (fl oz)	= 0.031 liquid qt	= 29.573 ml
1 US liquid pint (pt)	= 0.5 liquid qt	= 0.4731 l
1 US liquid quart (qt)	= 2 US liquid pt	= 0.9463 l
1 US gallon	= 4 US liquid qt	= 3.7854 l
1 milliliter (ml)	= 0.001 l	= 0.0338 fl oz
1 centiliter (d)	= 10 ml	= 0.338 fl oz
1 liter (l)	= 100 cl	= 0.2641 US gallon

Household capacity

1 teaspoon	= 1/6 fluid oz	= 4.9 ml
1 tablespoon	= 1/2 fluid oz	= 14.8 ml
1 cup	= 8 fluid oz	= 236.6 ml
1 pint (2 cups)	= 16 fluid oz	= 473.2 ml
1 quart	= 32 fluid oz	= 946.4 ml
1 gallon (4 quarts)	= 128 fluid oz	= 3.785 l

2008

January

1	T
2	W
3	T
4	F
5	S
6	S
7	M
8	T
9	W
10	T
11	F
12	S
13	S
14	M
15	T
16	W
17	T
18	F
19	S
20	S
21	M
22	T
23	W
24	T
25	F
26	S
27	S
28	M
29	T
30	W
31	T

February

1	F
2	S
3	S
4	M
5	T
6	W
7	T
8	F
9	S
10	S
11	M
12	T
13	W
14	T
15	F
16	S
17	S
18	M
19	T
20	W
21	T
22	F
23	S
24	S
25	M
26	T
27	W
28	T
29	F

March

1	S
2	S
3	M
4	T
5	W
6	T
7	F
8	S
9	S
10	M
11	T
12	W
13	T
14	F
15	S
16	S
17	M
18	T
19	W
20	T
21	F
22	S
23	S
24	M
25	T
26	W
27	T
28	F
29	S
30	S
31	M

April

1	T
2	W
3	T
4	F
5	S
6	S
7	M
8	T
9	W
10	T
11	F
12	S
13	S
14	M
15	T
16	W
17	T
18	F
19	S
20	S
21	M
22	T
23	W
24	T
25	F
26	S
27	S
28	M
29	T
30	W

May

1	T
2	F
3	S
4	S
5	M
6	T
7	W
8	T
9	F
10	S
11	S
12	M
13	T
14	W
15	T
16	F
17	S
18	S
19	M
20	T
21	W
22	T
23	F
24	S
25	S
26	M
27	T
28	W
29	T
30	F
31	S

June

1	S
2	M
3	T
4	W
5	T
6	F
7	S
8	S
9	M
10	T
11	W
12	T
13	F
14	S
15	S
16	M
17	T
18	W
19	T
20	F
21	S
22	S
23	M
24	T
25	W
26	T
27	F
28	S
29	S
30	M

2008

July

1 T
2 W
3 T
4 F
5 S
6 S
7 M
8 T
9 W
10 T
11 F
12 S
13 S
14 M
15 T
16 W
17 T
18 F
19 S
20 S
21 M
22 T
23 W
24 T
25 F
26 S
27 S
28 M
29 T
30 W
31 T

August

1 F
2 S
3 S
4 M
5 T
6 W
7 T
8 F
9 S
10 S
11 M
12 T
13 W
14 T
15 F
16 S
17 S
18 M
19 T
20 W
21 T
22 F
23 S
24 S
25 M
26 T
27 W
28 T
29 F
30 S
31 S

September

1 M
2 T
3 W
4 T
5 F
6 S
7 S
8 M
9 T
10 W
11 T
12 F
13 S
14 S
15 M
16 T
17 W
18 T
19 F
20 S
21 S
22 M
23 T
24 W
25 T
26 F
27 S
28 S
29 M
30 T

October

1 W
2 T
3 F
4 S
5 S
6 M
7 T
8 W
9 T
10 F
11 S
12 S
13 M
14 T
15 W
16 T
17 F
18 S
19 S
20 M
21 T
22 W
23 T
24 F
25 S
26 S
27 M
28 T
29 W
30 T
31 F

November

1 S
2 S
3 M
4 T
5 W
6 T
7 F
8 S
9 S
10 M
11 T
12 W
13 T
14 F
15 S
16 S
17 M
18 T
19 W
20 T
21 F
22 S
23 S
24 M
25 T
26 W
27 T
28 F
29 S
30 S

December

1 M
2 T
3 W
4 T
5 F
6 S
7 S
8 M
9 T
10 W
11 T
12 F
13 S
14 S
15 M
16 T
17 W
18 T
19 F
20 S
21 S
22 M
23 T
24 W
25 T
26 F
27 S
28 S
29 M
30 T
31 W

December 2007 / January 2008

31 Monday

(

New Year's Eve

1 Tuesday

New Year's Day 2008 • Last Day of Kwanzaa

2 Wednesday

Day After New Year's Day (Observed) (NZL, SCT)

3 Thursday

4 Friday

5 Saturday

6 Sunday

Feast of the Epiphany

DECEMBER 2007

S	M	T	W	T	F	S
						1
2	3	4	5	6	7	8
9	10	11	12	13	14	15
16	17	18	19	20	21	22
23	24	25	26	27	28	29
30	31					

JANUARY 2008

S	M	T	W	T	F	S
		1	2	3	4	5
6	7	8	9	10	11	12
13	14	15	16	17	18	19
20	21	22	23	24	25	26
27	28	29	30	31		

Week 1

7 Monday

8 Tuesday

●

9 Wednesday

Islamic New Year Begins at Sundown

10 Thursday

11 Friday

12 Saturday

13 Sunday

JANUARY

S	M	T	W	T	F	S
		1	2	3	4	5
6	7	8	9	10	11	12
13	14	15	16	17	18	19
20	21	22	23	24	25	26
27	28	29	30	31		

FEBRUARY

S	M	T	W	T	F	S
					1	2
3	4	5	6	7	8	9
10	11	12	13	14	15	16
17	18	19	20	21	22	23
24	25	26	27	28	29	

Week 2

January

XVIII – The Moon

As the median star between the Earth and the heavens, the Moon was and is considered capable of influencing the life of men, animals, and plants. It is the symbol of natural rhythms, of the transformation of elements, of time that passes periodically re-proposing everything. It is also said that this star governs memory, imagination, dreams, and visions. In a negative sense, it is the symbol of instinctivity, inconstancy, sorcery, and illnesses connected to water. In short, lunar dominion stands for the hidden side of our conscience. The Moon reminds us not to be influenced, to control our instincts and to value dreams and memory as basic elements of our personality and as instruments for inner knowledge.

January

S	M	T	W	T	F	S
		1	2	3	4	5
6	7	8	9	10	11	12
13	14	15	16	17	18	19
20	21	22	23	24	25	26
27	28	29	30	31		

February

S	M	T	W	T	F	S
					1	2
3	4	5	6	7	8	9
10	11	12	13	14	15	16
17	18	19	20	21	22	23
24	25	26	27	28	29	

Week 3

14 Monday

15 Tuesday
(

16 Wednesday

17 Thursday

18 Friday

Ashura Begins at Sundown

19 Saturday

20 Sunday

LA LUNA - THE MOON - LA LUNE - LA LUNA - DER MOND

RE DI COPPE - KING OF CHALICES - ROI DE COUPES - REY DE COPAS - KÖNIG DER KELCHE

January

21 Monday

Martin Luther King Jr.'s Birthday (Observed) (USA) • Wellington Anniversary (NZL)

22 Tuesday

○

23 Wednesday

24 Thursday

25 Friday

26 Saturday

Australia Day (AUS)

27 Sunday

King of Chalices
In Christian symbolism the number fourteen had significance in that the Easter of the Resurrection was celebrated on the Sunday following the fourteenth moon, calculated from the moment of Christ's birth. Therefore, fourteen represents spiritual transformation. Other very profound mysteries, but too complex to be summarized here, are hidden in the theosophic additions of the figures that give life to this number: matter (10+4), magic (9+5), intellect (7+7), mysticism (8+6). We can summarize by affirming that this King represents spiritual, psychological, and emotional stability, symbolized by the chalice that he holds; a power projected in nature and to the surrounding people, as the gesture of benediction by the King suggests.

JANUARY

S	M	T	W	T	F	S
		1	2	3	4	5
6	7	8	9	10	11	12
13	14	15	16	17	18	19
20	21	22	23	24	25	26
27	28	29	30	31		

FEBRUARY

S	M	T	W	T	F	S
					1	2
3	4	5	6	7	8	9
10	11	12	13	14	15	16
17	18	19	20	21	22	23
24	25	26	27	28	29	

Week 4

January / February

28 Monday
_____
_____
_____
_____

29 Tuesday
_____
_____
_____
_____
_____

30 Wednesday
☽
_____
_____
_____
_____
_____

31 Thursday
_____
_____
_____
_____
_____

1 Friday
_____
_____
_____
_____
_____

2 Saturday
_____
_____
_____
_____

3 Sunday
_____
_____
_____
_____

FEBRUARY

S	M	T	W	T	F	S
					1	2
3	4	5	6	7	8	9
10	11	12	13	14	15	16
17	18	19	20	21	22	23
24	25	26	27	28	29	

MARCH

S	M	T	W	T	F	S
						1
2	3	4	5	6	7	8
9	10	11	12	13	14	15
16	17	18	19	20	21	22
23	24	25	26	27	28	29
30	31					

Week 5

February

4 Monday

Nelson Anniversary (NZL)

5 Tuesday

Mardi Gras

6 Wednesday

Ash Wednesday • Waitangi Day (NZL)

7 Thursday

●

Chinese New Year — Year of the Rat

8 Friday

9 Saturday

3rd Day of Chinese New Year

10 Sunday

First Sunday of Lent

FEBRUARY						
S	M	T	W	T	F	S
					1	2
3	4	5	6	7	8	9
10	11	12	13	14	15	16
17	18	19	20	21	22	23
24	25	26	27	28	29	

MARCH						
S	M	T	W	T	F	S
						1
2	3	4	5	6	7	8
9	10	11	12	13	14	15
16	17	18	19	20	21	22
23	24	25	26	27	28	29
30	31					

Week 6

February

Knight of Swords
This image is pervaded by a sinister, obscure halo. The number thirteen is actually presented here by a decidedly negative character. The black horse is traditionally the bearer of death and destruction. There are numerous legends that talk about the diabolic horses that appear from the underworld to sow illness and ill fortune. Basically, this figure represents the natural equilibrium that is regenerated by violent actions. At times these actions occur due to conscious or unconscious intervention by humankind. It is not a coincidence that certain tragedies determine the passing over to a new state of affairs, a new alliance between individuals, families, or populations, to a wider order.

FEBRUARY

S	M	T	W	T	F	S
					1	2
3	4	5	6	7	8	9
10	11	12	13	14	15	16
17	18	19	20	21	22	23
24	25	26	27	28	29	

MARCH

S	M	T	W	T	F	S
						1
2	3	4	5	6	7	8
9	10	11	12	13	14	15
16	17	18	19	20	21	22
23	24	25	26	27	28	29
30	31					

Week 7

11 Monday

12 Tuesday

Lincoln's Birthday (USA)

13 Wednesday

14 Thursday

☽

St. Valentine's Day

15 Friday

16 Saturday

17 Sunday

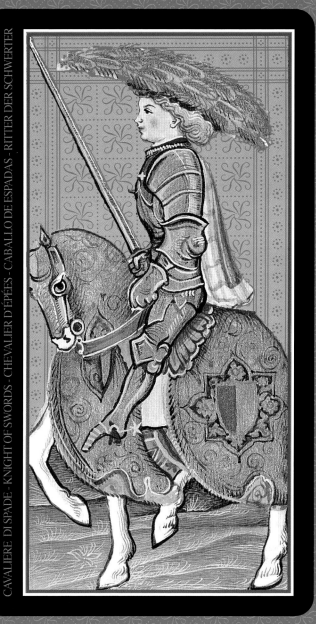

VI

GLI AMANTI - THE LOVERS - LES AMANTS - EL ENAMORADO - DIE LIEBENDEN

February

18 Monday

Presidents' Day (Observed) (USA) • Family Day — Provincial Alberta (CAN)

19 Tuesday

20 Wednesday

21 Thursday
○

22 Friday

Washington's Birthday (USA)

23 Saturday

24 Sunday

VI – The Lovers
Though present in all the old and modern tarot, the iconography of this card varied from one pack to another. In the Visconti pack, two young people are depicted holding hands in front of a fountain on which a young Cupid, winged and blindfolded, stands ready to shoot his darts. The promise or dawning of love, the noblest sentiment human beings can experience, is the meaning of this card, the moment in which rationality is abandoned and feeling or desire takes over. Choices that can be right or wrong derive from this and also, if desire is directed by reason and not by instinct, the possibility for interior realization which goes beyond the purely material, contingent dimension of existence.

FEBRUARY

S	M	T	W	T	F	S
					1	2
3	4	5	6	7	8	9
10	11	12	13	14	15	16
17	18	19	20	21	22	23
24	25	26	27	28	29	

MARCH

S	M	T	W	T	F	S
						1
2	3	4	5	6	7	8
9	10	11	12	13	14	15
16	17	18	19	20	21	22
23	24	25	26	27	28	29
30	31					

Week 8

February / March

25 Monday

26 Tuesday

27 Wednesday

28 Thursday

Friday

)

Saturday

St. David's Day

2 Sunday

Mothering Sunday (CAN, GBR, IRL, N IRL)

MARCH

S	M	T	W	T	F	S
						1
2	3	4	5	6	7	8
9	10	11	12	13	14	15
16	17	18	19	20	21	22
23	24	25	26	27	28	29
30	31					

APRIL

S	M	T	W	T	F	S
		1	2	3	4	5
6	7	8	9	10	11	12
13	14	15	16	17	18	19
20	21	22	23	24	25	26
27	28	29	30			

Week 9

3   Monday

Labour Day (W AUS)

4   Tuesday

5   Wednesday

6   Thursday

7   Friday

●

8   Saturday

International Women's Day

9   Sunday

Daylight Saving Time Begins (2:00 A.M.) (USA, CAN)

MARCH

S	M	T	W	T	F	S
						1
2	3	4	5	6	7	8
9	10	11	12	13	14	15
16	17	18	19	20	21	22
23	24	25	26	27	28	29
30	31					

APRIL

S	M	T	W	T	F	S
		1	2	3	4	5
6	7	8	9	10	11	12
13	14	15	16	17	18	19
20	21	22	23	24	25	26
27	28	29	30			

Week 10

March

XIV – Temperance

A woman in a star-spangled dress pours liquid from one jug to another. Traditional iconography of Temperance, a cardinal virtue, probably comes from the marriage at Cana, where Jesus instructs the servants to pour water from one jar to another, transforming it into wine (John, II, 6-9). There, water was transformed into a stimulating liquid. Here, a liquid is mixed with another to mitigate its force. According to medieval Christian interpretation, Temperance moderated sexuality and carnal pleasures, the fount of intellectual confusion and spiritual perdition. This figure attempts to resolve the conflict between body and spirit; in an immediate sense, to control irritability, master irrational instincts, and curb impulsiveness on the path to inner perfection.

March

S	M	T	W	T	F	S
						1
2	3	4	5	6	7	8
9	10	11	12	13	14	15
16	17	18	19	20	21	22
23	24	25	26	27	28	29
30	31					

April

S	M	T	W	T	F	S
		1	2	3	4	5
6	7	8	9	10	11	12
13	14	15	16	17	18	19
20	21	22	23	24	25	26
27	28	29	30			

Week 11

10 Monday

Orthodox Lent Begins • Commonwealth Day (CAN, AUS, GBR, N IRL)
Taranaki Anniversary (NZL) • Eight Hours Day (TAS AUS)

11 Tuesday

12 Wednesday

13 Thursday

14 Friday

15 Saturday

16 Sunday

Palm Sunday

LA TEMPERANZA - TEMPERANCE - LA TEMPÉRANCE - LA TEMPLANZA - DIE MÄSSIGKEIT

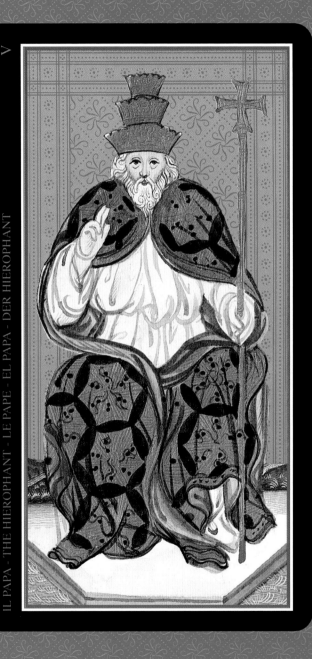

IL PAPA · THE HIEROPHANT · LE PAPE · EL PAPA · DER HIEROPHANT

17 Monday

St. Patrick's Day • Canberra Day (ACT, AUS)

18 Tuesday

19 Wednesday

Mohammed's Birthday Begins at Sundown

20 Thursday

First Day of Spring • Maundy Thursday • Purim Begins at Sundown

21 Friday

○

Good Friday • Bank Holiday (GBR, IRL, N IRL, SCT)

22 Saturday

23 Sunday

Easter

V – The Pope
The Pope is the highest spiritual authority in Catholic Christianity; the highest representative of God among humans in matters of faith and custom. Deeper symbolic meanings include religious vocation, theological learning and therefore higher knowledge, clarity, and illumination; as well as duty, whether moral or civil; rigour and tolerance; authority and goodness. Allegorically, the Pope is a person of unequivocal moral authority—the head of the family, the teacher, the guide, the wise man offering explanations, the mediator above all. This card refers again to the need to seek a higher power, this time of a moral or spiritual nature, in an effort to follow the path to knowledge and to perfect one's own being.

MARCH

S	M	T	W	T	F	S
						1
2	3	4	5	6	7	8
9	10	11	12	13	14	15
16	17	18	19	20	21	22
23	24	25	26	27	28	29
30	31					

APRIL

S	M	T	W	T	F	S
		1	2	3	4	5
6	7	8	9	10	11	12
13	14	15	16	17	18	19
20	21	22	23	24	25	26
27	28	29	30			

Week 12

March

24 Monday

Bank Holiday (CAN, GBR, N IRL, NZL) • Otago Anniversary (NZL)

25 Tuesday

Feast of the Annunciation

26 Wednesday

27 Thursday

28 Friday

29 Saturday

☽

30 Sunday

Summer Time Begins (EU)

MARCH

S	M	T	W	T	F	S
						1
2	3	4	5	6	7	8
9	10	11	12	13	14	15
16	17	18	19	20	21	22
23	24	25	26	27	28	29
30	31					

APRIL

S	M	T	W	T	F	S
		1	2	3	4	5
6	7	8	9	10	11	12
13	14	15	16	17	18	19
20	21	22	23	24	25	26
27	28	29	30			

Week 13

31 Monday

1 Tuesday

April Fools' Day

2 Wednesday

3 Thursday

4 Friday

5 Saturday

6 Sunday
●

APRIL						
S	M	T	W	T	F	S
		1	2	3	4	5
6	7	8	9	10	11	12
13	14	15	16	17	18	19
20	21	22	23	24	25	26
27	28	29	30			

MAY						
S	M	T	W	T	F	S
				1	2	3
4	5	6	7	8	9	10
11	12	13	14	15	16	17
18	19	20	21	22	23	24
25	26	27	28	29	30	31

Week 14

April

XX – Judgement

"And he shall send his angels with a great sound of a trumpet, and they shall gather together his elect from the four winds…"
"And the graves were opened; and many bodies of the saints which slept arose" (Matthew, XXIV, 31 and XXVII, 52). This image has changed little and it undoubtedly portrays the day of Judgement, the final battle between good and evil. Messages of renewal, rebirth also exist in this allegory—the reawakening of one's conscience, the overcoming of a closed or afflicted condition, an opening towards a new life. Be it worldly or otherworldly, reflect often on the assessment that waits at the end of each undertaking or trial, including the unique, unrepeatable experience of life itself.

APRIL

S	M	T	W	T	F	S
		1	2	3	4	5
6	7	8	9	10	11	12
13	14	15	16	17	18	19
20	21	22	23	24	25	26
27	28	29	30			

MAY

S	M	T	W	T	F	S
				1	2	3
4	5	6	7	8	9	10
11	12	13	14	15	16	17
18	19	20	21	22	23	24
25	26	27	28	29	30	31

Week 15

7 Monday

8 Tuesday

9 Wednesday

10 Thursday

11 Friday

12 Saturday

13 Sunday

IL GIUDIZIO - JUDGEMENT - LE JUGEMENT - EL JUICIO - GERICHT

XX

IL MONDO - THE WORLD - LE MONDE - EL MUNDO - DIE WELT

14 Monday

15 Tuesday

Tax Day (USA)

16 Wednesday

17 Thursday

18 Friday

19 Saturday

Passover Begins at Sundown

20 Sunday

○

XXI – The World
The angels holding a sphere containing a starry sky and an island castle are cherubim assigned by Christian tradition the task of sustaining the *primum mobile*, the outermost moving sphere of the universe. This allegory refers to the perfection of the Cosmos, and to the rapture of those who succeed in understanding God in themselves. In a material sense, this figure represents totality, completeness, the subtle relationship that binds various parts of reality together. It also stands for perfection, absolute peace, an absence of problems, tensions, and contradictions. It is the allegorical representation of Supreme Good—that Good which those who have followed an erroneous path will lack when they will assist Glory but not be part of it.

April

S	M	T	W	T	F	S
		1	2	3	4	5
6	7	8	9	10	11	12
13	14	15	16	17	18	19
20	21	22	23	24	25	26
27	28	29	30			

May

S	M	T	W	T	F	S
				1	2	3
4	5	6	7	8	9	10
11	12	13	14	15	16	17
18	19	20	21	22	23	24
25	26	27	28	29	30	31

Week 16

April

21 Monday

Birthday of Queen Elizabeth II

22 Tuesday

Earth Day

23 Wednesday

St. George's Day • Administrative Professionals' Day

24 Thursday

25 Friday

ANZAC Day (AUS, NZL) • Orthodox Holy Friday

26 Saturday

27 Sunday

Orthodox Easter • Last Day of Passover

APRIL

S	M	T	W	T	F	S
		1	2	3	4	5
6	7	8	9	10	11	12
13	14	15	16	17	18	19
20	21	22	23	24	25	26
27	28	29	30			

MAY

S	M	T	W	T	F	S
				1	2	3
4	5	6	7	8	9	10
11	12	13	14	15	16	17
18	19	20	21	22	23	24
25	26	27	28	29	30	31

Week 17

28 Monday

)

29 Tuesday

30 Wednesday

1 Thursday

May Day/Labour Day • Feast of the Ascension • National Day of Prayer (USA)

2 Friday

Holocaust Remembrance Day

3 Saturday

4 Sunday

MAY						
S	M	T	W	T	F	S
				1	2	3
4	5	6	7	8	9	10
11	12	13	14	15	16	17
18	19	20	21	22	23	24
25	26	27	28	29	30	31

JUNE						
S	M	T	W	T	F	S
1	2	3	4	5	6	7
8	9	10	11	12	13	14
15	16	17	18	19	20	21
22	23	24	25	26	27	28
29	30					

Week 18

May

IV – The Emperor

The Emperor is a necessary counterpart to the Empress, depicted as an elderly, bearded man, sumptuously dressed and seated on a throne. In his right hand he holds a sceptre and in his left a golden globe, symbols of temporal power. The Emperor represents the highest authority in an administrative field. Derived from this are the qualities of stability, order, equilibrium, and protection. Thus the Emperor, with the Empress, is a refuge (but this time of a material sort), and a symbol of fertility, a father to his dominion. The Emperor is the need to submit to a superior power of a material nature, with the aim of obtaining the necessary protection to bring to completion the pre-established undertakings to be realized.

MAY

S	M	T	W	T	F	S
				1	2	3
4	5	6	7	8	9	10
11	12	13	14	15	16	17
18	19	20	21	22	23	24
25	26	27	28	29	30	31

JUNE

S	M	T	W	T	F	S
1	2	3	4	5	6	7
8	9	10	11	12	13	14
15	16	17	18	19	20	21
22	23	24	25	26	27	28
29	30					

Week 19

---

5 Monday

●

Cinco de Mayo (MEX) • Bank Holiday (GBR, IRL, N IRL, NT AUS, SCT)

6 Tuesday

7 Wednesday

8 Thursday

9 Friday

10 Saturday

11 Sunday

Mother's Day (USA, CAN, AUS, NZL) • Pentecost

IV

L'IMPERATORE - THE EMPEROR - L'EMPEREUR - EL EMPERADOR - DER HERRSCHER

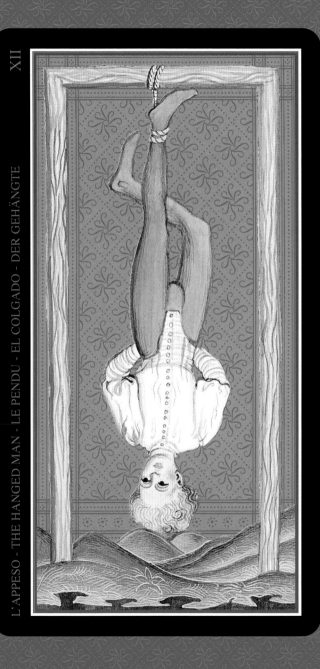

L'APPESO - THE HANGED MAN - LE PENDU - EL COLGADO - DER GEHÄNGTE

May

12 Monday

☾

International Nurses Day

13 Tuesday

14 Wednesday

15 Thursday

16 Friday

17 Saturday

Armed Forces Day (USA)

18 Sunday

XII – The Hanged Man
A man hangs by one foot from the beam of a gallows-like frame. Renaissance art has helped us understand this figure (at that time called "the Traitor"). In the Estensi Tarot of Charles VI, money falls from the hands of the hanging man, a reference to Judas's betrayal. Further defense can be found in the Bolognini Chapel in Bologna's church of San Petronio. A 1410 painting of Hell includes two men hanging by their feet with the words *ido/latria* next to them, referring to their betrayal of faith in the one God. Thus the symbolism is twofold: first, the error that gives rise to punishment, then, impotence, prison, wounded self-love, and the suffering that directly results from chastisement.

May

S	M	T	W	T	F	S
				1	2	3
4	5	6	7	8	9	10
11	12	13	14	15	16	17
18	19	20	21	22	23	24
25	26	27	28	29	30	31

June

S	M	T	W	T	F	S
1	2	3	4	5	6	7
8	9	10	11	12	13	14
15	16	17	18	19	20	21
22	23	24	25	26	27	28
29	30					

Week 20

May

19 Monday
_____
_____
_____
_____
_____
_____
Victoria Day (CAN) • Adelaide Cup Day (S AUS)

20 Tuesday
○
_____
_____
_____
_____
_____
_____

21 Wednesday
_____
_____
_____
_____
_____
_____

22 Thursday
_____
_____
_____
_____
_____
Lag B'Omer Begins at Sundown

23 Friday
_____
_____
_____
_____
_____
_____

24 Saturday
_____
_____
_____
_____

25 Sunday
_____
_____
_____
_____
_____

MAY

S	M	T	W	T	F	S
				1	2	3
4	5	6	7	8	9	10
11	12	13	14	15	16	17
18	19	20	21	22	23	24
25	26	27	28	29	30	31

JUNE

S	M	T	W	T	F	S
1	2	3	4	5	6	7
8	9	10	11	12	13	14
15	16	17	18	19	20	21
22	23	24	25	26	27	28
29	30					

Week 21

May / June

26 Monday

Memorial Day (Observed) (USA) • Bank Holiday (GBR, N IRL, SCT)

27 Tuesday

28 Wednesday
☽

29 Thursday

30 Friday

31 Saturday

1 Sunday

JUNE

S	M	T	W	T	F	S
1	2	3	4	5	6	7
8	9	10	11	12	13	14
15	16	17	18	19	20	21
22	23	24	25	26	27	28
29	30					

JULY

S	M	T	W	T	F	S
		1	2	3	4	5
6	7	8	9	10	11	12
13	14	15	16	17	18	19
20	21	22	23	24	25	26
27	28	29	30	31		

Week 22

June

III – The Empress

The Empress, seated on a throne, wears a crown and golden robes bearing emblems of the Visconti-Sforza family. She holds a small sceptre in her right hand and a shield bearing the imperial eagle in her left. In its entirety, this image refers to a well-defined female power that manifests itself in particular ways: seduction, subtle attraction for a presumed weakness, sentimentalism. In a wider sense, she represents birth, growth, and the evolution of humanity and of nature as a whole. Woman, as mother, represents fertility, and thus the Empress, whose dominion extends to the whole world, embodies this quality. She is the door beyond which the mystery of life is hidden—a refuge of consciousness, the font of intellectual inspiration.

JUNE

S	M	T	W	T	F	S
1	2	3	4	5	6	7
8	9	10	11	12	13	14
15	16	17	18	19	20	21
22	23	24	25	26	27	28
29	30					

JULY

S	M	T	W	T	F	S
		1	2	3	4	5
6	7	8	9	10	11	12
13	14	15	16	17	18	19
20	21	22	23	24	25	26
27	28	29	30	31		

Week 23

---

2 Monday

Queen's Birthday (NZL) • Bank Holiday (IRL) • Foundation Day (W AUS)

3 Tuesday

●

4 Wednesday

5 Thursday

World Environment Day

6 Friday

7 Saturday

8 Sunday

Shavuot Begins at Sundown

III

L'IMPERATRICE - THE EMPRESS - L'IMPÉRATRICE - LA EMPERATRIZ - DIE HERRSCHERIN

June

9 Monday

Queen's Birthday (AUS except W AUS)

10 Tuesday

☾

11 Wednesday

12 Thursday

13 Friday

14 Saturday

Flag Day (USA)

15 Sunday

Father's Day (USA, CAN, GBR, IRL, N IRL)

Knight of Chalices
The number twelve depicts divine order made manifest on Earth but still inaccessible, e.g., the apostles. It expresses the movement and the evolution ordained by matter and spirit according to the cyclic laws. It is the projection of the four cardinal points on three levels of being: spiritual, intellectual, and material. It also represents the multiplication of the four elements (earth, water, air, fire) for the three alchemic principles (sulphur, salt, mercury), or alternatively the conditions of man projected into the physical, psychic, and spiritual dimensions. This knight is therefore a messenger who could be heavenly, earthly, or from the underworld.

\	JUNE					
S	M	T	W	T	F	S
1	2	3	4	5	6	7
8	9	10	11	12	13	14
15	16	17	18	19	20	21
22	23	24	25	26	27	28
29	30					

\	JULY					
S	M	T	W	T	F	S
		1	2	3	4	5
6	7	8	9	10	11	12
13	14	15	16	17	18	19
20	21	22	23	24	25	26
27	28	29	30	31		

Week 24

June

16 Monday

17 Tuesday

18 Wednesday
○

19 Thursday

20 Friday

21 Saturday

First Day of Summer

22 Sunday

JUNE

S	M	T	W	T	F	S
1	2	3	4	5	6	7
8	9	10	11	12	13	14
15	16	17	18	19	20	21
22	23	24	25	26	27	28
29	30					

JULY

S	M	T	W	T	F	S
		1	2	3	4	5
6	7	8	9	10	11	12
13	14	15	16	17	18	19
20	21	22	23	24	25	26
27	28	29	30	31		

23 Monday

Newfoundland Discovery Day (CAN)

24 Tuesday

Saint-Jean-Baptiste Day (Quebec, CAN)

25 Wednesday

26 Thursday

☽

27 Friday

28 Saturday

29 Sunday

JUNE

S	M	T	W	T	F	S
1	2	3	4	5	6	7
8	9	10	11	12	13	14
15	16	17	18	19	20	21
22	23	24	25	26	27	28
29	30					

JULY

S	M	T	W	T	F	S
		1	2	3	4	5
6	7	8	9	10	11	12
13	14	15	16	17	18	19
20	21	22	23	24	25	26
27	28	29	30	31		

Week 26

June / July

XIX – The Sun

This winged figure parading a sun-face represents the medieval view of cosmology that linked celestial beings with planetary spheres. The sun's light eliminates shadows and brings clarity to the world, but it can also blind; its rays bring life to Earth when they do not burn it. Astrologers established the elements of a person's character from the sun's position at his birth and its relationship with the planets. The message of this card is simple. If man's fate is linked to the Sun, to rationality and clarity, it is imperative to shed light on oneself and the things around one. The ways out of difficulty, the routes toward success, the roads to glory, the paths toward knowledge are linked to individual intelligence and its applications.

JULY

S	M	T	W	T	F	S
		1	2	3	4	5
6	7	8	9	10	11	12
13	14	15	16	17	18	19
20	21	22	23	24	25	26
27	28	29	30	31		

AUGUST

S	M	T	W	T	F	S
					1	2
3	4	5	6	7	8	9
10	11	12	13	14	15	16
17	18	19	20	21	22	23
24	25	26	27	28	29	30
31						

Week 27

30 Monday

1 Tuesday

Canada Day (CAN)

2 Wednesday

3 Thursday

●

4 Friday

Independence Day (USA)

5 Saturday

6 Sunday

IL SOLE - THE SUN - LE SOLEIL - EL SOL - DIE SONNE

XIX

7 Monday

8 Tuesday

9 Wednesday

10 Thursday

☾

11 Friday

12 Saturday

13 Sunday

XI – Strength
Strength is one of the four cardinal virtues. In the Visconti Tarot, Strength is represented by a man wearing a protective cuirass who is about to club a lion. This is a common depiction of the first of Hercules' twelve labors, ending with his victory over the Nemean lion. Strength as courage must not be confused with reckless temerity. Implied here is moral steadiness, of ability in opposing evil forces with determination, of the will to continue along one's path while confronting remarkable obstacles. The deeper meaning is a struggle against oneself—imposing limits, renouncing those vanities and vices that can separate man from his civil and moral obligations and from those same existential struggles with which he must come to terms.

			JULY			
S	M	T	W	T	F	S
		1	2	3	4	5
6	7	8	9	10	11	12
13	14	15	16	17	18	19
20	21	22	23	24	25	26
27	28	29	30	31		

			AUGUST			
S	M	T	W	T	F	S
					1	2
3	4	5	6	7	8	9
10	11	12	13	14	15	16
17	18	19	20	21	22	23
24	25	26	27	28	29	30
31						

Week 28

July

14 Monday

Bastille Day (FRA)

15 Tuesday

16 Wednesday

17 Thursday

18 Friday

○

19 Saturday

20 Sunday

JULY

S	M	T	W	T	F	S
		1	2	3	4	5
6	7	8	9	10	11	12
13	14	15	16	17	18	19
20	21	22	23	24	25	26
27	28	29	30	31		

AUGUST

S	M	T	W	T	F	S
					1	2
3	4	5	6	7	8	9
10	11	12	13	14	15	16
17	18	19	20	21	22	23
24	25	26	27	28	29	30
31						

Week 29

July

21 Monday

22 Tuesday

23 Wednesday

24 Thursday

25 Friday
)

26 Saturday

27 Sunday

July

S	M	T	W	T	F	S
		1	2	3	4	5
6	7	8	9	10	11	12
13	14	15	16	17	18	19
20	21	22	23	24	25	26
27	28	29	30	31		

August

S	M	T	W	T	F	S
					1	2
3	4	5	6	7	8	9
10	11	12	13	14	15	16
17	18	19	20	21	22	23
24	25	26	27	28	29	30
31						

Week 30

July / August

Queen of Pentacles

Here the number thirteen refers to the control of intellectual energy and diverse states of consciousness. This control should follow precise ritual rules, but it is necessary to verify that it is in harmony with actual individual rhythms. The expansion of the awareness that derives from the manipulation of conscious states must be guided. This figure symbolizes the "coagulation" of mental energy that comes from an understanding of the values of the rite. But the affirmation of one's individuality is not the goal; rather it is the departure point for a new internal transformation that brings one to a more profound personal knowledge.

AUGUST						
S	M	T	W	T	F	S
					1	2
3	4	5	6	7	8	9
10	11	12	13	14	15	16
17	18	19	20	21	22	23
24	25	26	27	28	29	30
31						

SEPTEMBER						
S	M	T	W	T	F	S
	1	2	3	4	5	6
7	8	9	10	11	12	13
14	15	16	17	18	19	20
21	22	23	24	25	26	27
28	29	30				

Week 31

28 Monday

29 Tuesday

30 Wednesday

31 Thursday

1 Friday
●

2 Saturday

3 Sunday

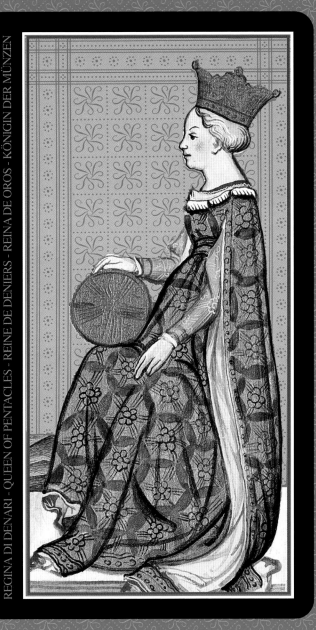

REGINA DI DENARI - QUEEN OF PENTACLES - REINE DE DENIERS - REINA DE OROS - KÖNIGIN DER MÜNZEN

4 Monday

_____
_____
_____
_____
_____

Bank Holiday (IRL, NSW, SCT) • Civic Holiday (CAN)

5 Tuesday

_____
_____
_____
_____
_____

6 Wednesday

_____
_____
_____
_____
_____

7 Thursday

_____
_____
_____
_____
_____

8 Friday

☾

_____
_____
_____
_____
_____

9 Saturday

_____
_____
_____
_____

Tisha B'av Begins at Sundown

10 Sunday

_____
_____
_____
_____
_____

I – The Magician

Contemporary tarot packs depict this image as a magician, but in the Visconti Tarot cards he is more simply a conjuror. Colorfully dressed in robes and furs, the Magician is seated at a table with the tools of his profession. He is a reference to human ability. This ability helps man to maneuver adroitly and intelligently, but also to cheat, falsify reality, and swindle his neighbor in an effort to win trust and money. It is a game requiring both parties: the fraud would not be possible without the consent of the individual participating in the challenge. By extension, the Magician is also an allegory for humankind's autonomy—his ability to manipulate and exploit available opportunities in his attempt to be the author of his own destiny.

AUGUST

S	M	T	W	T	F	S
					1	2
3	4	5	6	7	8	9
10	11	12	13	14	15	16
17	18	19	20	21	22	23
24	25	26	27	28	29	30
31						

SEPTEMBER

S	M	T	W	T	F	S
	1	2	3	4	5	6
7	8	9	10	11	12	13
14	15	16	17	18	19	20
21	22	23	24	25	26	27
28	29	30				

Week 32

August

11 Monday

12 Tuesday

International Youth Day

13 Wednesday

14 Thursday

15 Friday

Feast of the Assumption

16 Saturday

○

17 Sunday

AUGUST

S	M	T	W	T	F	S
					1	2
3	4	5	6	7	8	9
10	11	12	13	14	15	16
17	18	19	20	21	22	23
24	25	26	27	28	29	30
31						

SEPTEMBER

S	M	T	W	T	F	S
	1	2	3	4	5	6
7	8	9	10	11	12	13
14	15	16	17	18	19	20
21	22	23	24	25	26	27
28	29	30				

Week 33

18   Monday

Yukon Discovery Day (CAN)

19   Tuesday

20   Wednesday

21   Thursday

22   Friday

23   Saturday

)

24   Sunday

AUGUST

S	M	T	W	T	F	S
					1	2
3	4	5	6	7	8	9
10	11	12	13	14	15	16
17	18	19	20	21	22	23
24	25	26	27	28	29	30
31						

SEPTEMBER

S	M	T	W	T	F	S
	1	2	3	4	5	6
7	8	9	10	11	12	13
14	15	16	17	18	19	20
21	22	23	24	25	26	27
28	29	30				

Week 34

August

X – The Wheel of Fortune

The animal features represent displeasing attributes—ignorance, indolence—associated with those who attempt to rest on their laurels once they have obtained success and garnered earthly conquests. The human condition is precarious; sooner or later, the wheel will turn and conditions will change. The old man at the bottom of the wheel represents the cyclical movement of life and its changing situations. Time leads to an accumulation of experiences that become wisdom in old age. The wheel can turn at any moment, moved simply by chance or coincidence, but Dante Alighieri, paraphrasing Aristotle, said: "The more man succumbs to reason, the less he will succumb to fortune" (Convivio, IV, 11).

AUGUST						
S	M	T	W	T	F	S
					1	2
3	4	5	6	7	8	9
10	11	12	13	14	15	16
17	18	19	20	21	22	23
24	25	26	27	28	29	30
31						

SEPTEMBER						
S	M	T	W	T	F	S
	1	2	3	4	5	6
7	8	9	10	11	12	13
14	15	16	17	18	19	20
21	22	23	24	25	26	27
28	29	30				

Week 35

25 Monday

Bank Holiday (GBR, N IRL)

26 Tuesday

27 Wednesday

28 Thursday

29 Friday

30 Saturday

●

31 Sunday

LA RUOTA - THE WHEEL - LA ROUE DE FORTUNE - LA RUEDA - DAS RAD

LA PAPESSA - THE HIGH PRIESTESS - LA PAPESSE - LA SACERDOTISA - DIE HOHEPRIESTERIN   II

September

1 Monday

Labor Day (USA) • Labour Day (CAN) • Ramadan Begins at Sundown

2 Tuesday

3 Wednesday

4 Thursday

5 Friday

6 Saturday

7 Sunday

(

Grandparents Day (USA)

II – The High Priestess
The Visconti artist intended this image to represent an authentic Christian esotericism. The seated figure holds a cross in her right hand and a book in her left. She wears a papal tiara, but her typically monastic gown, tied with a waist rope, contrasts with the robes of the high ecclesiastical hierarchy. In Christianity, Faith is the highest moral value. Allegorically, the High Priestess represents the unconditional acceptance of Christian mysteries, those truths revealed by God that transcend human intelligence: the Unity and Trinity of God, the Incarnation, Passion, Death, and Resurrection of Christ, the Eucharist, the Immaculate Conception. Metaphorically, she stands for intuition, rigour, emotional control, and platonic love.

SEPTEMBER

S	M	T	W	T	F	S
	1	2	3	4	5	6
7	8	9	10	11	12	13
14	15	16	17	18	19	20
21	22	23	24	25	26	27
28	29	30				

OCTOBER

S	M	T	W	T	F	S
			1	2	3	4
5	6	7	8	9	10	11
12	13	14	15	16	17	18
19	20	21	22	23	24	25
26	27	28	29	30	31	

Week 36

September

8 Monday

9 Tuesday

10 Wednesday

11 Thursday

Patriot Day (USA)

12 Friday

13 Saturday

14 Sunday

SEPTEMBER

S	M	T	W	T	F	S
	1	2	3	4	5	6
7	8	9	10	11	12	13
14	15	16	17	18	19	20
21	22	23	24	25	26	27
28	29	30				

OCTOBER

S	M	T	W	T	F	S
			1	2	3	4
5	6	7	8	9	10	11
12	13	14	15	16	17	18
19	20	21	22	23	24	25
26	27	28	29	30	31	

15   Monday

○

16   Tuesday

17   Wednesday

Citizenship Day (USA)

18   Thursday

19   Friday

SEPTEMBER						
S	M	T	W	T	F	S
	1	2	3	4	5	6
7	8	9	10	11	12	13
14	15	16	17	18	19	20
21	22	23	24	25	26	27
28	29	30				

20   Saturday

OCTOBER						
S	M	T	W	T	F	S
			1	2	3	4
5	6	7	8	9	10	11
12	13	14	15	16	17	18
19	20	21	22	23	24	25
26	27	28	29	30	31	

21   Sunday

International Day of Peace

Week 38

September

IX – The Hermit
Similarities are evident between this hourglass-bearing hunchback and classical iconography for Saturn, the god of Time. The hourglass was later replaced by a lantern, and the figure, less richly clothed, became a sort of pilgrim called Hermit. The allegorical significance is *tempus fugit*. The wayfarer is the man who, proceeding on his existential path, meditates on the fleetingness of life and the true meaning of existence. He is a highly reflective person, aware of the limits—notably, time—that nature has imposed on human beings. Solitude, as a positive reflection on one's condition or as isolation, is also suggested. The individual must shape these qualities and make them useful for the journey to real knowledge.

SEPTEMBER						
S	M	T	W	T	F	S
	1	2	3	4	5	6
7	8	9	10	11	12	13
14	15	16	17	18	19	20
21	22	23	24	25	26	27
28	29	30				

OCTOBER						
S	M	T	W	T	F	S
			1	2	3	4
5	6	7	8	9	10	11
12	13	14	15	16	17	18
19	20	21	22	23	24	25
26	27	28	29	30	31	

22 Monday
)

First Day of Autumn

23 Tuesday

24 Wednesday

25 Thursday

26 Friday

Native American Day (USA)

27 Saturday

28 Sunday

Week 39

L'EREMITA · THE HERMIT · L'ERMITE · EL ERMITAÑO · DER EREMIT

LA GIUSTIZIA - JUSTICE - LA JUSTICE - LA JUSTICIA - GERECHTIGKEIT

29 Monday

●

Rosh Hashanah Begins at Sundown • Queen's Birthday (W AUS)

30 Tuesday

Eid-al-Fitr Begins at Sundown

1 Wednesday

2 Thursday

3 Friday

4 Saturday

5 Sunday

VIII – Justice

This crowned female has attributes that mirror those of the Greek goddess, Themis: scales for weighing and a sword for dividing. The motif recurs in Christian culture; Themis's instruments became attributes of the Archangel Michael, responsible for weighing souls during the Last Judgement. This card represents higher justice in the institutions that issue the laws on which civil society is based. But Justice, being a cardinal virtue, takes on a key role in an individual's intellectual and spiritual development. The scales represent the equilibrium between the parts in question, while the sword refers to power over oneself. This card, therefore, is discipline, adaptation, respect for the law and established order, and especially for interior order.

OCTOBER

S	M	T	W	T	F	S
			1	2	3	4
5	6	7	8	9	10	11
12	13	14	15	16	17	18
19	20	21	22	23	24	25
26	27	28	29	30	31	

NOVEMBER

S	M	T	W	T	F	S
						1
2	3	4	5	6	7	8
9	10	11	12	13	14	15
16	17	18	19	20	21	22
23	24	25	26	27	28	29
30						

Week 40

October

6 Monday

Labour Day (S AUS)

7 Tuesday

☾

8 Wednesday

Yom Kippur Begins at Sundown

9 Thursday

10 Friday

11 Saturday

12 Sunday

Children's Day (USA)

OCTOBER

S	M	T	W	T	F	S
			1	2	3	4
5	6	7	8	9	10	11
12	13	14	15	16	17	18
19	20	21	22	23	24	25
26	27	28	29	30	31	

NOVEMBER

S	M	T	W	T	F	S
						1
2	3	4	5	6	7	8
9	10	11	12	13	14	15
16	17	18	19	20	21	22
23	24	25	26	27	28	29
30						

Week 41

October

13 Monday

Columbus Day (Observed) (USA) • Thanksgiving Day (CAN)
Sukkot Begins at Sundown

14 Tuesday

○

15 Wednesday

16 Thursday

17 Friday

Hawkes Bay Anniversary (NZL)

18 Saturday

19 Sunday

S	M	T	W	T	F	S
			1	2	3	4
5	6	7	8	9	10	11
12	13	14	15	16	17	18
19	20	21	22	23	24	25
26	27	28	29	30	31	

NOVEMBER

S	M	T	W	T	F	S
						1
2	3	4	5	6	7	8
9	10	11	12	13	14	15
16	17	18	19	20	21	22
23	24	25	26	27	28	29
30						

Week 42

October

XVI – The Tower

The original of this card is lost from the Visconti pack, but two references of the same period exist: in the "Tarot of Charles VI," the Tower has been struck by lightning that flashes from a black cloud and shatters the massive fortress. In the "Rothschild Sheet," the lightning strikes a castle, hurling two men to the ground. The "House" struck by lightning stands for divine punishment; lightning is not a simple natural calamity but an unstoppable destructive force delivered from the heavens. This card symbolizes the collapse of certainties, security, defenses; it represents a fall. The warnings expressed by the preceding cards, especially Death and the Devil, advise that the ruin awaiting habitual wrongdoers is sufficiently clear.

OCTOBER

S	M	T	W	T	F	S
			1	2	3	4
5	6	7	8	9	10	11
12	13	14	15	16	17	18
19	20	21	22	23	24	25
26	27	28	29	30	31	

NOVEMBER

S	M	T	W	T	F	S
						1
2	3	4	5	6	7	8
9	10	11	12	13	14	15
16	17	18	19	20	21	22
23	24	25	26	27	28	29
30						

Week 43

---

20 Monday

Shemini Atzeret Begins at Sundown

21 Tuesday

)

Simchat Torah Begins at Sundown

22 Wednesday

23 Thursday

24 Friday

United Nations Day

25 Saturday

26 Sunday

Summer Time Ends (EU)

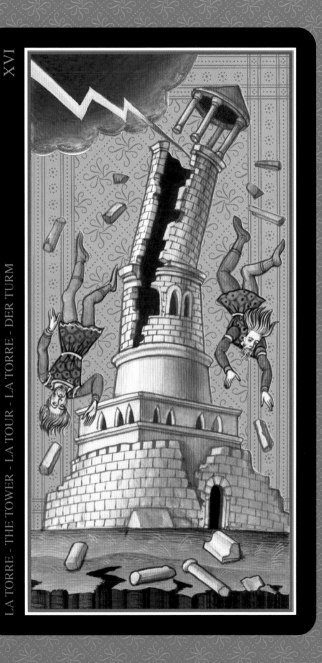

XVI

LA TORRE - THE TOWER - LA TOUR - LA TORRE - DER TURM

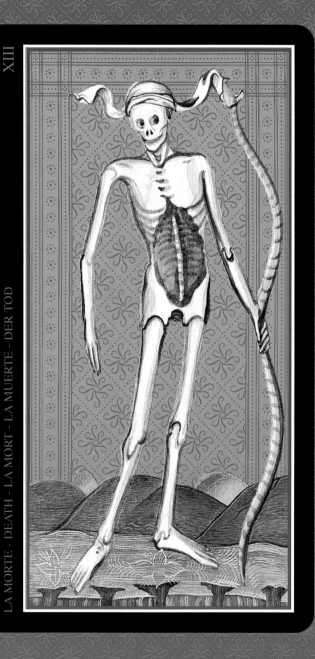

LA MORTE - DEATH - LA MORT - LA MUERTE - DER TOD

27 Monday

Labour Day (NZL) • Bank Holiday (IRL)

28 Tuesday

●

29 Wednesday

30 Thursday

31 Friday

Halloween

1 Saturday

All Saints' Day

2 Sunday

All Souls' Day • Daylight Saving Time Ends (2:00 A.M.) (USA, CAN)

XIII – Death

In the Visconti Tarot, Death is depicted as a skeleton with a white bandage wound around its skull and holding a large bow in its left hand and an arrow in its right. It is defined as a warning, a sort of *memento mori* to recall the transience of earthly life and the futility of material conquests. Death for most is a tragic, inevitable fact; the end of everything. Metaphorically, this figure is a symbol for any inescapable, though not necessarily tragic, event: the sudden drastic ending of a situation, an unexpected change that radically clears away all past things. By not considering death the end of everything, we interpret it as an evolutionary passage whose mark, whether positive or negative, remains in the hands of the single individual.

NOVEMBER

S	M	T	W	T	F	S
						1
2	3	4	5	6	7	8
9	10	11	12	13	14	15
16	17	18	19	20	21	22
23	24	25	26	27	28	29
30						

DECEMBER

S	M	T	W	T	F	S
	1	2	3	4	5	6
7	8	9	10	11	12	13
14	15	16	17	18	19	20
21	22	23	24	25	26	27
28	29	30	31			

Week 44

November

3 Monday

Marlborough Anniversary (NZL)

4 Tuesday

Election Day (USA) • Melbourne Cup Day (AUS)

5 Wednesday

Guy Fawkes Day (GBR, N IRL)

6 Thursday

☽

7 Friday

8 Saturday

9 Sunday

Remembrance Sunday (GBR, N IRL)

November

S	M	T	W	T	F	S
						1
2	3	4	5	6	7	8
9	10	11	12	13	14	15
16	17	18	19	20	21	22
23	24	25	26	27	28	29
30						

December

S	M	T	W	T	F	S
	1	2	3	4	5	6
7	8	9	10	11	12	13
14	15	16	17	18	19	20
21	22	23	24	25	26	27
28	29	30	31			

Week 45

November

10 Monday

11 Tuesday

Veterans' Day (USA) • Armistice Day
Remembrance Day (CAN, AUS, GBR, N IRL, NZL)

12 Wednesday

13 Thursday

○

14 Friday

15 Saturday

16 Sunday

NOVEMBER

S	M	T	W	T	F	S
						1
2	3	4	5	6	7	8
9	10	11	12	13	14	15
16	17	18	19	20	21	22
23	24	25	26	27	28	29
30						

DECEMBER

S	M	T	W	T	F	S
	1	2	3	4	5	6
7	8	9	10	11	12	13
14	15	16	17	18	19	20
21	22	23	24	25	26	27
28	29	30	31			

Week 46

November

Queen of Wands

The Queen of Wands symbolizes benevolence and affection, but only as functions of the sense of security she wishes to impose on herself and the people around her. Her policy could be defined as an "iron fist in a velvet glove." She is a despot, but restricted only to her kingdom—usually the home and the workplace. However, this could be expanded to national and international levels, if she obtains important political or economic duties. At the same time the Queen of Wands is a simple person, cordial, open to dialogue, sensitive to the problems of those near her, if these do not risk involving her, her family, or her "kingdom," in which case she could close up and even become threatening.

NOVEMBER

S	M	T	W	T	F	S
						1
2	3	4	5	6	7	8
9	10	11	12	13	14	15
16	17	18	19	20	21	22
23	24	25	26	27	28	29
30						

DECEMBER

S	M	T	W	T	F	S
	1	2	3	4	5	6
7	8	9	10	11	12	13
14	15	16	17	18	19	20
21	22	23	24	25	26	27
28	29	30	31			

Week 47

17 Monday

18 Tuesday

19 Wednesday
)

20 Thursday

21 Friday

22 Saturday

23 Sunday

REGINA DI BASTONI - QUEEN OF WANDS - REINE DE BÂTONS - REINA DE BASTOS - KÖNIGIN DER STÄBE

24 Monday

25 Tuesday

26 Wednesday

27 Thursday
●

Thanksgiving Day (USA)

28 Friday

29 Saturday

30 Sunday

First Sunday of Advent • St. Andrew's Day

King of Swords
This ruler represents the supreme authority of the Physical World, in that the force of weapons is superior to any other force. From any perspective, the right "to life and death" of all creatures is unjustifiable, as life comes from the Creator; but as this law has never been respected by humans, an authority capable of preventing crimes and punishing them has always been necessary. The power of the King, theoretically, should move in an equal manner in all directions of the universe, but this would be Utopia. Therefore, this figure represents the universal laws in the Spiritual World; the justice man is never capable of applying in the Intellectual World; the power that settles controversies, but also is able to nourish itself in the Physical World.

NOVEMBER

S	M	T	W	T	F	S
						1
2	3	4	5	6	7	8
9	10	11	12	13	14	15
16	17	18	19	20	21	22
23	24	25	26	27	28	29
30						

DECEMBER

S	M	T	W	T	F	S
	1	2	3	4	5	6
7	8	9	10	11	12	13
14	15	16	17	18	19	20
21	22	23	24	25	26	27
28	29	30	31			

Week 48

December

1 Monday

World AIDS Day • Westland Anniversary (NZL)

2 Tuesday

3 Wednesday

4 Thursday

5 Friday
☾

6 Saturday

7 Sunday

Pearl Harbor Remembrance Day • Eid-al-Adha Begins at Sundown

DECEMBER

S	M	T	W	T	F	S
	1	2	3	4	5	6
7	8	9	10	11	12	13
14	15	16	17	18	19	20
21	22	23	24	25	26	27
28	29	30	31			

JANUARY 2009

S	M	T	W	T	F	S
				1	2	3
4	5	6	7	8	9	10
11	12	13	14	15	16	17
18	19	20	21	22	23	24
25	26	27	28	29	30	31

Week 49

8   Monday

9   Tuesday

10   Wednesday

Human Rights Day

11   Thursday

12   Friday

○

13   Saturday

14   Sunday

DECEMBER

S	M	T	W	T	F	S
	1	2	3	4	5	6
7	8	9	10	11	12	13
14	15	16	17	18	19	20
21	22	23	24	25	26	27
28	29	30	31			

JANUARY 2009

S	M	T	W	T	F	S
				1	2	3
4	5	6	7	8	9	10
11	12	13	14	15	16	17
18	19	20	21	22	23	24
25	26	27	28	29	30	31

Week 50

December

VII – The Chariot
This depiction is unique to the Visconti pack. A queen is seated on a two-wheeled chariot pulled by winged horses. In other versions a warrior replaces the woman. The image refers directly to the Roman military tradition of parading victorious consuls to the Campidoglio. Allegorically, the female driver is Glory and Fame, typical of the period. Apart from the allegory, this card means victory, triumph, success, progress—military concepts conveyed to an ethical or moral sense. Triumph also refers to the challenges we face every day and successfully overcome.
The individual who drives the triumphal chariot is one who succeeds in dominating himself and his environment by continually channeling energy in the desired direction.

DECEMBER

S	M	T	W	T	F	S
		1	2	3	4	5	6
7	8	9	10	11	12	13
14	15	16	17	18	19	20
21	22	23	24	25	26	27
28	29	30	31			

JANUARY 2009

S	M	T	W	T	F	S
				1	2	3
4	5	6	7	8	9	10
11	12	13	14	15	16	17
18	19	20	21	22	23	24
25	26	27	28	29	30	31

Week 51

15 Monday

16 Tuesday

17 Wednesday

18 Thursday

19 Friday
)

20 Saturday

21 Sunday

First Day of Winter • Hanukkah Begins at Sundown

VII

IL CARRO · THE CHARIOT · LE CHAR · EL CARRO · DER WAGEN

XVII

LE STELLE - THE STARS - LES ÉTOILES - LA ESTRELLA - DER STERN

22 Monday

_____
_____
_____
_____

23 Tuesday

_____
_____
_____
_____
_____

24 Wednesday

_____
_____
_____
_____

Christmas Eve

25 Thursday

_____
_____
_____
_____

Christmas Day

26 Friday

_____
_____
_____
_____

St. Stephen's Day • Boxing Day/Bank Holiday (AUS, GBR, IRL, N IRL, NZL)
First Day of Kwanzaa

27 Saturday

●

_____
_____
_____
_____
_____

28 Sunday

_____
_____
_____
_____

Islamic New Year Begins at Sundown

XVII – The Star

A woman wearing a blue dress and a red star-studded cloak holds an eight-pointed star in her left hand. This astral symbol traditionally referred to Venus, the most luminous star with the Sun and the Moon. In a general context, this trump does not offer any particular interpretative difficulties. Think of Dante's journey: after visiting hell, Dante and Virgil "came forth to look once more upon the stars." The good star that indicates the way upwards after death is represented here, but she also symbolizes beauty, art, games, and above all the love that guides living beings. She is a figure of peace, goodness, and serenity. In a general sense, she is hope, favorable prospects, and harmony between people, recreation and pleasure of the senses.

DECEMBER

S	M	T	W	T	F	S
	1	2	3	4	5	6
7	8	9	10	11	12	13
14	15	16	17	18	19	20
21	22	23	24	25	26	27
28	29	30	31			

JANUARY 2009

S	M	T	W	T	F	S
				1	2	3
4	5	6	7	8	9	10
11	12	13	14	15	16	17
18	19	20	21	22	23	24
25	26	27	28	29	30	31

Week 52

December / January 2009

29 Monday

30 Tuesday

31 Wednesday

New Year's Eve

1 Thursday

New Year's Day 2009 • Last Day of Kwanzaa

2 Friday

Day After New Year's Day (Observed) (NZL, SCT)

3 Saturday

4 Sunday

JANUARY 2009

S	M	T	W	T	F	S
				1	2	3
4	5	6	7	8	9	10
11	12	13	14	15	16	17
18	19	20	21	22	23	24
25	26	27	28	29	30	31

FEBRUARY 2009

S	M	T	W	T	F	S
1	2	3	4	5	6	7
8	9	10	11	12	13	14
15	16	17	18	19	20	21
22	23	24	25	26	27	28

Week 1

5   Monday

6   Tuesday

Feast of the Epiphany

7   Wednesday

8   Thursday

9   Friday

10   Saturday

○

11   Sunday

JANUARY 2009

S	M	T	W	T	F	S
				1	2	3
4	5	6	7	8	9	10
11	12	13	14	15	16	17
18	19	20	21	22	23	24
25	26	27	28	29	30	31

FEBRUARY 2009

S	M	T	W	T	F	S
1	2	3	4	5	6	7
8	9	10	11	12	13	14
15	16	17	18	19	20	21
22	23	24	25	26	27	28

Week 2

2009

January

S	M	T	W	T	F	S
				1	2	3
4	5	6	7	8	9	10
11	12	13	14	15	16	17
18	19	20	21	22	23	24
25	26	27	28	29	30	31

February

S	M	T	W	T	F	S
1	2	3	4	5	6	7
8	9	10	11	12	13	14
15	16	17	18	19	20	21
22	23	24	25	26	27	28

March

S	M	T	W	T	F	S
1	2	3	4	5	6	7
8	9	10	11	12	13	14
15	16	17	18	19	20	21
22	23	24	25	26	27	28
29	30	31				

April

S	M	T	W	T	F	S
			1	2	3	4
5	6	7	8	9	10	11
12	13	14	15	16	17	18
19	20	21	22	23	24	25
26	27	28	29	30		

May

S	M	T	W	T	F	S
					1	2
3	4	5	6	7	8	9
10	11	12	13	14	15	16
17	18	19	20	21	22	23
24	25	26	27	28	29	30
31						

June

S	M	T	W	T	F	S
	1	2	3	4	5	6
7	8	9	10	11	12	13
14	15	16	17	18	19	20
21	22	23	24	25	26	27
28	29	30				

July

S	M	T	W	T	F	S
			1	2	3	4
5	6	7	8	9	10	11
12	13	14	15	16	17	18
19	20	21	22	23	24	25
26	27	28	29	30	31	

August

S	M	T	W	T	F	S
						1
2	3	4	5	6	7	8
9	10	11	12	13	14	15
16	17	18	19	20	21	22
23	24	25	26	27	28	29
30	31					

September

S	M	T	W	T	F	S
		1	2	3	4	5
6	7	8	9	10	11	12
13	14	15	16	17	18	19
20	21	22	23	24	25	26
27	28	29	30			

October

S	M	T	W	T	F	S
				1	2	3
4	5	6	7	8	9	10
11	12	13	14	15	16	17
18	19	20	21	22	23	24
25	26	27	28	29	30	31

November

S	M	T	W	T	F	S
1	2	3	4	5	6	7
8	9	10	11	12	13	14
15	16	17	18	19	20	21
22	23	24	25	26	27	28
29	30					

December

S	M	T	W	T	F	S
		1	2	3	4	5
6	7	8	9	10	11	12
13	14	15	16	17	18	19
20	21	22	23	24	25	26
27	28	29	30	31		

2009

January

SUNDAY	MONDAY	TUESDAY	WEDNESDAY	THURSDAY	FRIDAY	SATURDAY
				1	2	3
4	5	6	7	8	9	10
11	12	13	14	15	16	17
18	19	20	21	22	23	24
25	26	27	28	29	30	31

February

SUNDAY	MONDAY	TUESDAY	WEDNESDAY	THURSDAY	FRIDAY	SATURDAY
1	2	3	4	5	6	7
8	9	10	11	12	13	14
15	16	17	18	19	20	21
22	23	24	25	26	27	28

2009

March

Sunday	Monday	Tuesday	Wednesday	Thursday	Friday	Saturday
1	2	3	4	5	6	7
8	9	10	11	12	13	14
15	16	17	18	19	20	21
22	23	24	25	26	27	28
29	30	31				

April

Sunday	Monday	Tuesday	Wednesday	Thursday	Friday	Saturday
			1	2	3	4
5	6	7	8	9	10	11
12	13	14	15	16	17	18
19	20	21	22	23	24	25
26	27	28	29	30		

May

SUNDAY	MONDAY	TUESDAY	WEDNESDAY	THURSDAY	FRIDAY	SATURDAY
					1	2
3	4	5	6	7	8	9
10	11	12	13	14	15	16
17	18	19	20	21	22	23
24/31	25	26	27	28	29	30

June

SUNDAY	MONDAY	TUESDAY	WEDNESDAY	THURSDAY	FRIDAY	SATURDAY
	1	2	3	4	5	6
7	8	9	10	11	12	13
14	15	16	17	18	19	20
21	22	23	24	25	26	27
28	29	30				

2009

July

SUNDAY	MONDAY	TUESDAY	WEDNESDAY	THURSDAY	FRIDAY	SATURDAY
			1	2	3	4
5	6	7	8	9	10	11
12	13	14	15	16	17	18
19	20	21	22	23	24	25
26	27	28	29	30	31	

August

SUNDAY	MONDAY	TUESDAY	WEDNESDAY	THURSDAY	FRIDAY	SATURDAY
						1
2	3	4	5	6	7	8
9	10	11	12	13	14	15
16	17	18	19	20	21	22
23/30	24/31	25	26	27	28	29

2009

September

SUNDAY	MONDAY	TUESDAY	WEDNESDAY	THURSDAY	FRIDAY	SATURDAY
		1	2	3	4	5
6	7	8	9	10	11	12
13	14	15	16	17	18	19
20	21	22	23	24	25	26
27	28	29	30			

October

SUNDAY	MONDAY	TUESDAY	WEDNESDAY	THURSDAY	FRIDAY	SATURDAY
				1	2	3
4	5	6	7	8	9	10
11	12	13	14	15	16	17
18	19	20	21	22	23	24
25	26	27	28	29	30	31

2009

November

SUNDAY	MONDAY	TUESDAY	WEDNESDAY	THURSDAY	FRIDAY	SATURDAY
1	2	3	4	5	6	7
8	9	10	11	12	13	14
15	16	17	18	19	20	21
22	23	24	25	26	27	28
29	30					

December

SUNDAY	MONDAY	TUESDAY	WEDNESDAY	THURSDAY	FRIDAY	SATURDAY
		1	2	3	4	5
6	7	8	9	10	11	12
13	14	15	16	17	18	19
20	21	22	23	24	25	26
27	28	29	30	31		

Notes

Notes

Notes

Notes

Notes

Notes

Notes

Notes